Mulan, Warrior

Mulan, Woman Warrior
木蘭女戰士

An Easy-to-Read Story in Traditional Chinese and Pinyin,
233 Word Vocabulary Level

by Jeff Pepper

IMAGIN8
PRESS

Published in the United States by Imagin8 Press LLC, Verona, Pennsylvania, US. For information, contact us via email at info@imagin8press.com, or visit www.imagin8press.com.

Our books may be purchased directly in quantity at a reduced price, visit www.imagin8press.com for details.

Imagin8 Press, the Imagin8 logo and the sail image are all trademarks of Imagin8 Press LLC.

Written by Jeff Pepper
Edited by Xiao Hui Wang
Cover and book design by Jeff Pepper
Artwork by Next Mars Media, Luoyang, China
Audiobook narration by Junyou Chen

ISBN: 978-1733165099
Version 309

Audiobook

A complete Chinese language audio version of this book is available free of charge. To access it, go to YouTube.com and search for the Imagin8 Press channel. There you will find free audiobooks for this and most of our other books.

You can also visit our website, www.imagin8press.com, to find a direct link to the audiobook and information about our other books.

Introduction

The story of Mulan, the young girl who joins the army to save her family and her country, is at least 1500 years old. Nobody knows when the story was first told. The first written record of the story is *The Ballad of Mulan* from the sixth century. That folk song was told in 31 couplets, a format which we have followed, more or less, in this book's 30 six-line verses.

Over the centuries, the story of Mulan has inspired dozens of poems, plays, novels, songs, and more recently, graphic novels, TV shows and films. The details of the story vary, but the core is always the same: a young girl living with her family in a small Chinese village learns that the army requires each family to contribute one man to fight invaders from the North. To save her elderly father she disguises herself as a young man and enlists in the army; she excels at fighting, strategy and leadership and rises through the ranks; the war ends successfully; she is recognized as a hero and is offered rewards by the

Emperor; she declines the rewards and humbly chooses to return to her family and take up the traditional life of a village woman.

Mulan's story tells us a lot about women in traditional Chinese society. China was male-dominated, though not as much as some other cultures. Families were led by men, though a widow could assume temporary leadership until her oldest son came of age. Men could divorce their wives for any of seven different reasons, but a woman could only divorce her husband if he agreed. And property was passed on from father to son, bypassing wives and daughters.

The most extreme form of female subservience was foot binding, where a young girl's feet were tightly wrapped in cloth to prevent them from growing to normal size, thus making the girl appear more beautiful but also less mobile and less able to do daily chores. Originally limited to the wealthy elite, foot binding eventually spread throughout China.

The Chinese revolution in 1911 and the communist rise to power in 1949 changed most of this. Foot binding was outlawed, parents no longer controlled marriage, and inheritance laws applied equally to women and men. Mao Zedong's famous dictum, "Women hold up half the sky", helped to shift women into more or less equal roles to men, though Chinese women were (and still are) expected to at least give the appearance of being subservient to men.

So on the one hand, Mulan is a breaker of traditions, a liberated woman in a male dominated society, saving her country and her family. But looking deeper, the Mulan story is not as radical as it first appears. Mulan saves her country and her family, but she does it as a man. And when the time comes for her to be rewarded, does she reveal herself to be a woman and accept her rewards from the Emperor and become a female army general (or assume a high civil post, as described in some versions)? No. She reveals herself as a woman, and then she humbly chooses to take on the traditional role of a woman, returning to her village and, we assume, becoming a wife and mother.

And so, Mulan shows us both the power of the Chinese woman (slayer of invaders, leader of troops, hero of the nation) but also the limitations.

In our telling of the Mulan story, we remain faithful to the core story and tell how she returns to her village, but as to what her life is like afterwards, we leave that open for you to imagine!

There are many versions of Mulan, but our goal here is to combine a great story with an opportunity to learn to read Simplified Chinese. To do that, we've limited the vocabulary that we use, telling the story with only 240 different words using fewer than 300 total characters. We also make the reading a bit easier by underlining proper nouns, and defining new words (those not included in the standard HSK-3 word list) on the page where they first appear. Each page of Chinese also contains the pinyin (romanized spelling) version. This gives an assist to beginning readers by letting them sound out the words instead of having to recognize each character. The pinyin is also useful for looking up the meaning of words in the glossary, which is sorted alphabetically by pinyin. And there's an English translation at the end.

We are grateful to our friends at NextMars Media for their terrific illustrations. And thanks to Xiao Hui Wang for her careful review of the manuscript.

We hope you enjoy this book! We have lots of other books for beginning and intermediate Chinese readers, see our website www.imagin8press.com to learn more. And feel free to contact us at info@imagin8press.com.

Jeff Pepper
Pittsburgh, Pennsylvania

木蘭女戰士

Mùlán Nǚ Zhànshì

我叫木蘭。

我叫<u>木蘭</u>，我姓<u>花</u>。

今年夏天，我就十七歲了。

我喜歡騎馬和用劍。

人們說女孩不應該做這些事。

但是我不聽，

因為我喜歡騎馬和打仗。

騎　　qí – to ride

劍　　jiàn – sword

打仗　dǎzhàng – to fight

Wǒ jiào Mùlán, wǒ xìng Huā.
Jīnnián xiàtiān, wǒ jiù shíqī suì le.
Wǒ xǐhuān qímǎ hé yòng jiàn.
Rénmen shuō nǚhái bù yīnggāi zuò zhèxiē shì.
Dànshì wǒ bù tīng,
yīnwèi wǒ xǐhuān qímǎ hé dǎzhàng.

他教我打仗。

我的家在中國北方。
我爸爸年輕的時候在軍隊裡。
他現在老了，但是他教我騎馬和打仗。
我和爸爸媽媽、弟弟、妹妹住在一起。
我還有一個哥哥，他叫平，
但是他在我十二歲的時候死了。

北	běi – north	
軍隊	jūnduì – army	
死	sǐ – die, dead	

Wǒ de jiā zài Zhōngguó běifāng.
Wǒ bàba niánqīng de shíhóu, zài jūnduì lǐ.
Tā xiànzài lǎo le, dànshì tā jiào wǒ qímǎ hé dǎzhàng.
Wǒ hé bàba māmā, dìdì hé mèimei zhù zài yìqǐ.
Wǒ hái yǒu yīgè gēgē, tā jiào Píng,
Dànshì tā zài wǒ shí'èr suì de shíhòu sǐ le.

這是我們的家!

今天有一個士兵來到我們家。
他說我們的國家有危險。
長城的北邊住著匈奴人。
他們的土地不好。
他們看到了我們的好土地。
他們想要它，但是這是我們的家！

士兵　　shìbīng – soldier
危險　　wéixiǎn – danger
長城　　chángchéng – Great Wall
土地　　tǔdì – land

Jīntiān yǒu yīgè shìbīng láidào wǒmen jiā.
Tā shuō wǒmen de guójiā yǒu wéixiǎn.
Chángchéng de běibiān zhùzhe Xiōngnú rén.
Tāmen de tǔdì bù hǎo.
Tāmen kàndào le wǒmen de hǎo tǔdì.
Tāmen xiǎng yào tā, dànshì zhè shì wǒmen de jiā!

我爸爸想去。

現在，每家都必須有一個人去軍隊。

我爸爸想去，但是他太老了。

我的弟弟想去，但是他祇是一個男孩。

怎麼才能讓我家有一個男人去軍隊呢？

我知道我怎麼能幫助我的家和國家。

但是我的爸爸媽媽不會喜歡的。

Xiànzài, měi jiā dōu bìxū yǒu yīgè rén qù jūnduì.
Wǒ bàba xiǎng qù, dànshì tā tài lǎo le.
Wǒ de dìdì xiǎng qù, dànshì tā zhǐshì yīgè nánhái.
Zěnme cáinéng ràng wǒjiā yǒu yī gè nánrén qù jūnduì ne?
Wǒ zhīdào wǒ zěnme néng bāngzhù wǒ de jiā hé guójiā.
Dànshì wǒ de bàba māmā bù huì xǐhuān de.

"不，你不能去。"

我告訴爸爸我想去軍隊。
他說，“不，你不能去。”
我告訴媽媽我想去軍隊。
她說，“不，你不能去。”
但是我必須幫助我的家和國家。
所以我說我不會聽他們的。

Wǒ gàosù bàba wǒ xiǎng qù jūnduì.
Tā shuō, "Bù, nǐ bùnéng qù."
Wǒ gàosù māmā wǒ xiǎng qù jūnduì.
Tā shuō, "Bù, nǐ bùnéng qù."
Dànshì wǒ bìxū bāngzhù wǒ de jiā hé guójiā.
Suǒyǐ wǒ shuō wǒ bù huì tīng tāmen de.

我会打仗。

我騎馬會比村裡的男孩快。
我打仗會比村裡的男孩好。
我的國家需要幫助，
軍隊需要年輕人。
所以雖然我是一個女孩，
我知道我應該做什麼。

村　　　cūn – village

Wǒ qímǎ huì bǐ cūnlǐ de nánhái kuài.
Wǒ dǎzhàng huì bǐ cūnlǐ de nánhái hǎo.
Wǒ de guójiā xūyào bāngzhù,
Jūnduì xūyào niánqīng rén.
Suǒyǐ suīrán wǒ shì yīgè nǚhái,
Wǒ zhīdào wǒ yīnggāi zuò shénme.

我要剪頭髮。

我要剪頭髮，換衣服。
我會學習去像個年輕男人。
我會學習像年輕男人一樣說話。
人們看著我，看到的會是一個年輕男人。
我還會改我的名字。
他們會叫我花平，不是花木蘭。

剪　　jiǎn – to cut
改　　gǎi – change

我爸爸不高興。

現在我必須去告訴我的爸爸媽媽。

我媽媽哭著說，一個女孩不能去軍隊。

我爸爸不高興，但是我想他明白。

他們說一個女孩應該在家裡。

他們說我不能去。

但是我說我的國家需要我的幫助。

Xiànzài wǒ bìxū qù gàosù wǒ de bàba māmā.
Wǒ māmā kūzhe shuō, yīgè nǚhái bùnéng qù jūnduì.
Wǒ bàba bù gāoxìng, dànshì wǒ xiǎng tā míngbai.
Tāmen shuō yīgè nǚhái yīnggāi zài jiālǐ.
Tāmen shuō wǒ bùnéng qù.
Dànshì wǒ shuō wǒ de guójiā xūyào wǒ de bāngzhù.

我剪了頭髮。

我剪了頭髮，現在我的頭髮很短。

我換了衣服，現在它們是年輕男人的衣服。

在我的衣服下面，我用布包在身體上。

我想我現在像個年輕男人。

但是士兵看到的會是男人還是女人？

我不知道。

布　　　bù – cloth

Wǒ jiǎn le tóufǎ, xiànzài wǒ de tóufǎ hěn duǎn.
Wǒ huàn le yīfú, xiànzài tāmen shì niánqīng nánrén de yīfú.
Zài wǒ de yīfú xiàmiàn, wǒ yòng bù bāo zài shēntǐ shàng.
Wǒ xiǎng wǒ xiànzài xiàng ge niánqīng nánrén.
Dànshì shìbīng kàndào de huì shì nánrén háishì nǚrén?
Wǒ bù zhīdào.

"我是來幫助我的国家。"

我拿了家裡的劍，說再見。

我很快走到軍營。

我說，“我是來幫助我的國家。”

高大的將軍看著我。

“你是一個漂亮的年輕人，但是很小。

你會用劍嗎？”

營　　yíng – camp

將軍　jiāngjūn – General

Wǒ ná le jiālǐ de jiàn, shuō zàijiàn.
Wǒ hěn kuài zǒu dào jūnyíng.
Wǒ shuō, "Wǒ shì lái bāngzhù wǒ de guójiā."
Gāodà de jiāngjūn kànzhe wǒ.
"Nǐ shì yīgè piàoliang de niánqīng rén, dànshì hěn xiǎo.
Nǐ huì yòng jiàn ma?"

"您就會看到！"

"您試試，您就會看到！"我說。

我用兩隻手拿著劍。

將軍用一隻手拿著劍。

很多士兵在看著我們。

將軍向我走來。

我們開始用劍戰鬥。

試　　shì – try
手　　shǒu – hand

"Nín shì shì, nín jiù huì kàn dào!" wǒ shuō.

Wǒ yòng liǎng zhī shǒu názhe jiàn.

Jiāngjūn yòng yī zhī shǒu názhe jiàn.

Hěnduō shìbīng zài kànzhe wǒmen.

Jiāngjūn xiàng wǒ zǒu lái.

Wǒmen kāishǐ yòng jiàn zhàndòu.

他想打我的頭！

他想打我的右邊，但是我擋住了。
他想打我的左邊，但是我擋住了。
右，左，左，右，我都擋住了。
然後他想打我的頭！
我很快把我的劍向上拿。
我的劍打他的劍，他的劍飛了。

擋住　dǎngzhù – to block
飛　　fēi – to fly

Tā xiǎng dǎ wǒ de yòubiān, dànshì wǒ dǎngzhù le.
Tā xiǎng dǎ wǒ de zuǒbiān, dànshì wǒ dǎngzhù le.
Yòu, zuǒ, zuǒ, yòu, wǒ dōu dǎngzhù le.
Ránhòu tā xiǎng dǎ wǒ de tóu!
Wǒ hěn kuài bǎ wǒ de jiàn xiàngshàng ná.
Wǒ de jiàn dǎ tā de jiàn, tā de jiàn fēi le.

我也很累。

我們站著，他看著我，我看著他。
然後將軍笑了。
"很好，我看到你會打仗！
我們需要好的士兵來幫助我們的國家。"
他走了，他很累。
我也很累，但是很高興。

Wǒmen zhànzhe, tā kànzhe wǒ, wǒ kànzhe tā.
Ránhòu jiāngjūn xiào le.
"Hěn hǎo, wǒ kàndào nǐ huì dǎzhàng!
Wǒmen xūyào hǎo de shìbīng lái bāngzhù wǒmen de guójiā."
Tā zǒu le, tā hěn lèi.
Wǒ yě hěn lèi, dànshì hěn gāoxìng.

"不用擔心，"我說。

軍隊把我分在十二人小隊裡。

其他士兵都看到了我和將軍的戰鬥。

他們都不敢和我說話！

我祇是對他們笑。

"不用擔心，"我說，"我是你們的朋友。

我們要一起保護我們的國家。"

小隊　xiǎoduì – squad

Jūnduì bǎ wǒ fēn zài shí'èr rén xiǎoduì lǐ.
Qítā shìbīng dōu kàndào le wǒ hé jiāngjūn de zhàndòu.
Tāmen dōu bù gǎn hé wǒ shuōhuà!
Wǒ zhǐshì duì tāmen xiào.
"Bùyòng dānxīn," wǒ shuō, "wǒ shì nǐmen de péngyǒu.
Wǒmen yào yìqǐ bǎohù wǒmen de guójiā."

我非常小心。

我非常小心，因為我是女孩。

早上，我一個人洗澡。

晚上，我一個人睡在地上。

我總是穿著我的衣服。

其他士兵祇是認為我有點害羞。

他們知道我能戰鬥，所以這不是問題。

害羞　hàixiū – shy

Wǒ fēicháng xiǎoxīn, yīnwèi wǒ shì nǚhái.
Zǎoshang, wǒ yīgè rén xǐzǎo.
Wǎnshàng, wǒ yīgè rén shuì zài dìshàng.
Wǒ zǒngshì chuānzhe wǒ de yīfú.
Qítā shìbīng zhǐshì rènwéi wǒ yǒudiǎn hàixiū.
Tāmen zhīdào wǒ néng zhàndòu, suǒyǐ zhè bùshì wèntí.

我帶著士兵戰鬥。

有一天，來了很多匈奴士兵。

他們有二十個，但是我們祇有十二個。

我們都很害怕，但是我們在為我們的國家戰鬥。

匈奴人逃了，但是我們沒有再追他們。

將軍看見我帶著士兵戰鬥。

他讓我做小隊長。

怕	pà – afraid
逃	táo – to escape
追	zhuī – to chase
長	zhǎng – leader

Yǒu yītiān, lái le hěnduō Xiōngnú shìbīng.

Tāmen yǒu èrshí gè, dànshì wǒmen zhǐyǒu shí'èr gè.

Wǒmen dōu hěn hàipà, dànshì wǒmen zài wèi wǒmen de guójiā zhàndòu.

Xiōngnú rén táo le, dànshì wǒmen méiyǒu zài zhuī tāmen.

Jiāngjūn kànjiàn wǒ dàizhe shìbīng zhàndòu.

Tā ràng wǒ zuò xiǎo duìzhǎng.

我帶 112 個士兵。

四年過去了，我學到了很多。

我是一個好戰士，一個好的小隊長。

我們多次和匈奴打仗，我們都贏了。

將軍喜歡我這個小隊長。

他讓我做旅長。

現在我帶 112 個士兵。

戰士　　zhànshì – warrior
贏　　　yíng – to win
旅　　　lǚ – brigade

Sì nián guòqù le, wǒ xuédào le hěnduō.
Wǒ shì yīgè hào zhànshì, yīgè hǎo de xiǎoduìzhǎng.
Wǒmen duō cì hé Xiōngnú dǎzhàng, wǒmen dōu yíng le.
Jiāngjūn xǐhuān wǒ zhège xiǎoduìzhǎng.
Tā ràng wǒ zuò lǚ zhǎng.
Xiànzài wǒ dài 112 gè shìbīng.

他們想進中國。

又過了八年。
現在，我的旅在長城南邊。
匈奴軍隊在長城北邊。
我們知道他們想進中國。
但是我們不知道他們會怎麼做。
我們必須知道他們的打算。

Yòu guò le bā nián.
Xiànzài, wǒ de lǚ zài chángchéng nán biān.
Xiōngnú jūnduì zài chángchéng běi biān.
Wǒmen zhīdào tāmen xiǎng jìn Zhōngguó.
Dànshì wǒmen bù zhīdào tāmen huì zěnme zuò.
Wǒmen bìxū zhīdào tāmen de dǎsuàn.

我們越過長城。

"我會去的，"我告訴將軍。
我讓兩個士兵和我一起去。
我們等到晚上，然後越過長城。
我們向北走，直到看到匈奴軍營。
軍營中有幾千個匈奴士兵。
我不知道我們怎麼和他們戰鬥。

"Wǒ huì qù de," wǒ gàosù jiāngjūn.
Wǒ ràng liǎng gè shìbīng hé wǒ yìqǐ qù.
Wǒmen děngdào wǎnshàng, ránhòu yuèguò chángchéng.
Wǒmen xiàng běi zǒu, zhídào kàn dào Xiōngnú jūnyíng.
Jūnyíng zhōng yǒu jǐ qiān gè Xiōngnú shìbīng.
Wǒ bù zhīdào wǒmen zěnme hé tāmen zhàndòu.

我穿著黑衣服。

我說，“我們必須知道他們的打算。”
“你們等在這裡。我去看看。”
我一個人去匈奴軍營裡。
我穿著黑衣服和黑鞋。
沒有人看到我，沒有人聽到我。
我看到一個大帳篷，走了過去。

帳篷　zhàngpéng – tent

Wǒ shuō, "Wǒmen bìxū zhīdào tāmen de dǎsuàn."
"Nǐmen děng zài zhèlǐ. Wǒ qù kànkan."
Wǒ yīgè rén qù Xiōngnú jūnyíng lǐ.
Wǒ chuānzhe hēi yīfú hé hēi xié.
Méiyǒu rén kàndào wǒ, méiyǒu rén tīngdào wǒ.
Wǒ kàndào yīgè dà zhàngpéng, zǒu le guòqù.

我聽到匈奴。

我把耳朵放在帳篷上。
我聽到匈奴將軍在和一些人說話。
他說，“我們明天要進中國。
我們要去附近的一條河，
在大馬山和小馬山中間。
在那裡，我們要走在長城下！”

河　　hé – river

Wǒ bǎ ěrduo fàng zài zhàngpéng shàng.
Wǒ tīngdào Xiōngnú jiāngjūn zài hé yīxiē rén shuōhuà.
Tā shuō, "Wǒmen míngtiān yào jìn Zhōngguó.
Wǒmen yào qù fùjìn de yītiáo hé,
Zài Dà Mǎ shān hé Xiǎo Mǎ shān zhōngjiān.
Zài nàlǐ, wǒmen yào zǒu zài chángchéng xià!"

"讓士兵們都起來。"

我和士兵們很快回到了我們的軍營。
將軍問我，“匈奴將軍說了什麼？”
我告訴將軍我聽到的。
他安靜地坐了幾分鐘。
然後他很快站起來，說，“讓士兵們都起來。”
我們都去河邊的一個地方。

起來　qǐlái – continue an action

Wǒ hé shìbīngmen hěn kuài huídào le wǒmen de jūnyíng.
Jiāngjūn wèn wǒ, "Xiōngnú jiāngjūn shuō le shénme?"
Wǒ gàosù jiāngjūn wǒ tīng dào de.
Tā ānjìng de zuò le jǐ fēnzhōng.
Ránhòu tā hěn kuài zhàn qǐlái, shuō, "Ràng shìbīngmen dōu qǐlái."
Wǒmen dōu qù hé biān de yīgè dìfāng.

我們等著他們。

早上，匈奴軍隊開始走在長城下。
但是我們的軍隊正在等著他們。
兩個軍隊都很大，都很會打仗。
他們戰鬥了很長時間，但是我們贏了。
匈奴軍隊回到長城北邊。
我很高興地說，我們再也見不到他們了！

Zǎoshàng, Xiōngnú jūnduì kāishǐ zǒu zài chángchéng xià.
Dànshì wǒmen de jūnduì zhèngzài děngzhe tāmen.
Liǎng ge jūnduì dōu hěn dà, dōu hěn huì dǎzhàng.
Tāmen zhàndòu le hěn cháng shíjiān, dànshì wǒmen yíng le.
Xiōngnú jūnduì huí dào chángchéng běibiān.
Wǒ hěn gāoxìng de shuō, wǒmen zài yě jiànbúdào tāmen le!

我們見了皇帝。

現在戰鬥結束了。

將軍讓我做營長。

現在我帶 1,120 個士兵。

我們一起去北京見皇帝。

我和將軍一起站在皇帝前面。

皇帝感謝我們，給我們禮物。

皇帝　　huángdì – emperor
感謝　　gǎnxiè – to thank
禮物　　lǐwù – gift

Xiànzài zhàndòu jiéshù le.
Jiāngjūn ràng wǒ zuò yíng zhǎng.
Xiànzài wǒ dài 1,120 gè shìbīng.
Wǒmen yìqǐ qù Běijīng jiàn huángdì.
Wǒ hé jiāngjūn yìqǐ zhàn zài huángdì qiánmiàn.
Huángdì gǎnxiè wǒmen, gěi wǒmen lǐwù.

“當然，”皇帝笑著說。

他要求我不要離開軍隊。

我說，"謝謝您，但是現在我們的國家沒有危險了。

我想回到我的家和我們的村。"

"當然，"皇帝笑著說。

他讓將軍和我一起回我家。

我以前小隊的士兵們跟我一起回家。

Tā yāoqiú wǒ búyào líkāi jūnduì.
Wǒ shuō, "Xièxiè nín, dànshì xiànzài wǒmen de guójiā méiyǒu wéixiǎn le.
Wǒ xiǎng huí dào wǒ de jiā hé wǒmen de cūn."
"Dāngrán," huángdì xiàozhe shuō.
Tā ràng jiāngjūn hé wǒ yìqǐ huí wǒjiā.
Wǒ yǐqián xiǎoduì de shìbīngmen gēn wǒ yìqǐ huí jiā.

"木蘭，你回家了！"

我們走了一個星期，然後我們到了我的村。
我們來到我的家。
我的家人知道我們回來了。
我們到的時侯，他們都站在我的家門前面。
每個人都在快樂地哭著。
他們說，"木蘭，你回家了！"

Wǒmen zǒu le yīgè xīngqī, ránhòu wǒmen dào le wǒ de cūn.
Wǒmen lái dào wǒ de jiā.
Wǒ de jiārén zhīdào wǒmen huílái le.
Wǒmen dào de shíhóu, tāmen dōu zhàn zài wǒ de jiā mén qiánmiàn.
Měigè rén dōu zài kuàilè de kūzhe.
Tāmen shuō, "Mùlán, nǐ huí jiā le!"

妹妹倒茶。

將軍看著我。 "誰是木蘭？" 他問。
"我會告訴您的，" 我說，"但是請進來。"
我們都進來了。
我的妹妹給將軍和士兵們倒茶。
我的弟弟害羞地站著，看著士兵們。
我走進房間洗澡，穿上女人的衣服。

倒　　　dào – to pour

Jiāngjūn kànzhe wǒ. "Shéi shì Mùlán?" tā wèn.
"Wǒ huì gàosù nín de," wǒ shuō, "dànshì qǐng jìn lái."
Wǒmen dōu jìn lái le.
Wǒ de mèimei gěi jiāngjūn hé shìbīngmen dào chá.
Wǒ de dìdì hàixiū de zhànzhe, kànzhe shìbīngmen.
Wǒ zǒu jìn fángjiān xǐzǎo, chuān shàng nǚrén de yīfú.

士兵開始大笑。

我出來看其他人。

"您好，將軍，"我說。

"我是花木蘭。我是村裡的一個女孩。"

將軍和士兵們都看著我，沒有人說話。

然後，一個士兵開始大笑。

他說，"我一直都知道你是一個漂亮的年輕人！"

Wǒ chūlái kàn qítā rén.

"Nín hǎo, jiāngjūn," wǒ shuō.

"Wǒ shì Huā Mùlán. Wǒ shì cūnlǐ de yīgè nǚhái."

Jiāngjūn hé shìbīngmen dōu kànzhe wǒ, méiyǒu rén shuōhuà.

Ránhòu, yīgè shìbīng kāishǐ dà xiào.

Tā shuō, "Wǒ yīzhí dōu zhīdào nǐ shì yīgè piàoliang de niánqīng rén!"

他們吃晚飯。

將軍和士兵們跟我們一起吃晚飯。
他們講我的事。
他們講和匈奴人打仗的事。
我爸爸問了很多問題。
我媽媽祇是安靜地坐著笑著。
每個人都很高興我又回家了。

晚飯　wǎnfàn – dinner

Jiāngjūn hé shìbīngmen gēn wǒmen yìqǐ chī wǎnfàn.
Tāmen jiǎng wǒ de shì.
Tāmen jiǎng hé Xiōngnú rén dǎzhàng de shì.
Wǒ bàba wèn le hěnduō wèntí.
Wǒ māmā zhǐshì ānjìng de zuòzhe xiàozhe.
Měigè rén dōu hěn gāoxìng wǒ yòu huí jiā le.

我什麼都可以做！

晚飯以後，將軍和士兵們準備離開。

"你是一個非常好的士兵，"將軍說。

我說，"我很高興能保護我們的國家。"

現在，我已經離開了軍隊。

我現在要做什麼呢？我不知道。

但是我知道我什麼都可以做！

Wǎnfàn yǐhòu, jiāngjūn hé shìbīngmen zhǔnbèi líkāi.
"Nǐ shì yīgè fēicháng hǎo de shìbīng," jiāngjūn shuō.
Wǒ shuō, "Wǒ hěn gāoxìng néng bǎohù wǒmen de guójiā."
Xiànzài, wǒ yǐjīng líkāi le jūnduì.
Wǒ xiànzài yào zuò shénme ne? Wǒ bù zhīdào.
Dànshì wǒ zhīdào wǒ shénme dōu kěyǐ zuò!

Mulan, Woman Warrior

My name is Mulan. My family name is Hua.
This summer I will be seventeen years old.
I love to ride my horse and use my sword.
People say that a girl should not do these things.
But I don't listen to them,
Because I love to ride and fight.

My family lives in northern China.
When my father was young, he was in the army.
He is old now, but he teaches me to ride and fight.
I live with my parents, younger brother and younger sister.
I also had an older brother named Ping,
But he died when I was 12 years old.

Today a soldier came to our house.
He said our country is in danger.
North of the Great Wall live the Hun people.
Their land is not good.
They have seen our good land.
They want it, but this is our home!

Now every family must give one man to the army.
My father wants to go, but he is too old.
My younger brother wants to go, but he is just a boy.
How can my family give a man to the army?
I know how I can help my family and country.
But my parents will not like it.

I tell my father that I want to be a soldier.
He says, "No, you cannot."
I tell my mother that I want to be a soldier.
She says, "No, you cannot."
But I must help my family and country.
So I say I will not listen to them.

I can ride faster than the village boys.
I can fight better than the village boys.
My country needs help,
And the army needs young men.
So though I am a young woman,
I know what I must do.

I will cut my hair and change my clothing.
I will learn to look like a young man.
I will learn to talk like a young man.
People will look at me and see a young man.
I will also change my name.
They will call me Hua Ping, not Hua Mulan.

Now I must go and tell my parents.
My mother cries and says a girl cannot join the army.
My father is not happy, but I think he understands.
They say a girl must stay home.
They say I cannot go.
But I say my country needs my help.

I cut my hair, now it is short.
I change my clothes, now they are a young man's clothes.
Under my clothes, I wrap cloth around my body.
Now I think I look like a young man.
But will the soldiers see a man or a woman?
I don't know.

I pick up my family's sword and I say goodbye.
Quickly I walk to the army camp.
"I am here to help my country," I say.
The tall army general looks down at me.
"You are a good looking young man, but very small.
Can you use a sword?"

"Just try, you will see!" I shout.
I pick up the sword and hold it in both hands.
The general holds his sword in one hand.
Many soldiers are watching us.
The general comes at me.
We begin to fight with our swords.

He tries to hit my right side, but I block.
He tries to hit my left side, but I block.
Right, left, left, right, I block them all.
Then he tries to hit my head!
Quickly I bring up my sword.
It hits his sword, and his sword flies away.

We stand and look at each other.
Then the general smiles.
"Good," he says. "I see you can fight!
We need good fighters to help our country."
He walks away, looking tired.
I am also tired, but very happy.

The army puts me in a twelve-man squad.
The other soldiers all saw the fight.
They are all afraid to talk to me!
I just smile at them.
"Don't worry," I say, "I am your friend.
Together we will keep our country safe."

I am very careful because I am a girl.
In the morning, I wash alone.
At night, I sleep alone on the ground.
I always wear my clothes.
The other soldiers just think that I am a little shy.
They know I can fight, so it's not a problem.

One day we run into a large group of Hun soldiers.
There are twenty of them, but only twelve of us.
We are all very afraid, but we fight for our country.
The Huns run away, but we do not try to catch them.
The general sees me leading the soldiers.
He makes me squad leader.

Four years pass. I learn a lot.
I am a good soldier and a good squad leader.
We meet the Huns many times, and we win.
The general likes how I lead my squad.
He asks me to be brigade leader.
Now I lead 112 soldiers.

Eight more years pass.
Now my brigade is just south of the Great Wall.
The Hun army is just north of the Great Wall.
We know that they want to enter China.
But we do not know how they will do it.
We must learn their plans.

"I will go," I tell the general.
I ask two soldiers to go with me.
We wait until night, then we cross the Great Wall.
We walk north until we see the Hun camp.
There are thousands of Hun soldiers in the camp.
I don't know how we can fight them all.

"We must know their plans," I say.
"You wait here. I will go and take a look."
I go alone into the middle of the Hun camp.
I wear black clothing and black shoes.
Nobody sees me, nobody hears me.
I see a large tent, and I walk up to it.

I put my ear up against the tent.
I hear the Hun general talking with some people.
He says, "We will enter China tomorrow.
We will go to a nearby river,
Between Big Horse Mountain and Little Horse Mountain.
There, we go under the Wall!"

The soldiers and I return quickly to our camp.

The general asks me, "What did the Hun general say?"

I tell the general what I heard.

He sits quietly for a few minutes.

Then he stands up quickly, and says, "Wake up all the soldiers."

We all go to a place near the river.

In the morning, the Hun army begins to cross under the Great Wall.

But our army is waiting for them.

Both armies are very large, and both know how to fight.

The battle lasts for a long time, but finally we win.

The Hun army returns to north of the Great Wall.

I am happy to say that we never see them again!

Now the fighting is over.

The general asks me to be battalion commander.

Now I lead 1,120 soldiers.

Together, we go to Beijing to meet the Emperor.

The general and I stand together in front of the Emperor.

The Emperor thanks us and gives us gifts.

He asks me to stay in the army.

"Thank you," I say, "But now our country is no longer in danger.

I want to return home to my family and village. "

"Of course," smiles the Emperor.

He asks the general to go with me to my home.

The soldiers from my first squad come with us.

We walk for a week, then we arrive at my village.

We come to my family's house.

My family knows that we are coming.

We arrive, and they are all standing in front of the house.

Everyone is crying happily.

"Mulan," they say, "You have come home!"

The general looks at me. "Who is Mulan?" he asks.

"I will tell you," I say. "But please come inside."

We all go into the house.

My little sister pours tea for the general and the soldiers.

My little brother stands shyly and watches the soldiers.

I go into my room to wash and put on my old clothes.

I come out to see the others.
"Hello General," I say, "I am Hua Mulan. I am a village girl."
The general and the soldiers all just look at me.
Nobody says anything.
Then a soldier starts to laugh.
He says, "I always knew you were a good looking guy!"

The general and the soldiers all eat dinner with us.
They tell stories about me.
They tell stories about the fights with the Huns.
My father asks many questions.
My mother just sits quietly and smiles.
Everyone is so happy that I am home again.

After dinner, the general and soldiers prepare to leave.
"You are a very good soldier," says the general.
I say, "I am glad I could protect our country."
Now my life as a soldier is finished.
What will I do now? I don't know.
But I know that I can do anything!

Glossary

These are all the Chinese words used in this book.

Chinese	Pinyin	English
安靜	ānjìng	quiet
把	bǎ	to hold, to guard, a bundle
八	bā	eight
爸爸	bàba	father
辦	bàn	to move
幫助	bāngzhù	to help
包	bāo	to wrap
保護	bǎohù	protection
北	běi	north
北京	Běijīng	Beijing
比	bǐ	compared to
邊	biān	side
必須	bìxū	must, need to
布	bù	cloth
不	bù	no, not, do not
不用	bùyòng	no need to

Chinese	Pinyin	English
茶	chá	tea
長	cháng	long
長城	chángchéng	Great Wall
吃	chī	to eat
出	chū	to go out
穿(著)	chuān(zhuó)	to wear
次	cì	next in a sequence
村	cūn	village
大	dà	big
打	dǎ	to hit, to play
帶(著)	dài(zhe)	to lead
當然	dāngrán	of course
擋住	dǎngzhù	to block
但是	dànshì	but
擔心	dānxīn	to worry
到	dào	to arrive, towards
倒	dào	to pour

打算	dǎsuàn	intend
打仗	dǎzhàng	to fight
的	de	of
的時候	deshíhòu	when
弟弟	dìdì	younger brother
地方	dìfāng	local area
都	dōu	all
短	duǎn	short
對	duì	correct, towards
多	duō	many
二	èr	two
耳朵	ěrduǒ	ear
放	fāng	to place
飛	fēi	to fly
非常	fēicháng	very much
分鐘	fēnzhōng	minute
附近	fùjìn	nearby
敢	gǎn	to dare
感謝	gǎnxiè	thank
高大	gāo dà	tall
告訴	gàosù	to tell

高興	gāoxìng	happy
個	gè	(measure word, generic)
哥哥	gēgē	older brother
給	gěi	to give
過	guò	to pass
國家	guójiā	country
過去	guòqù	in the past
還	hái	also
還有	hái yǒu	and also
害怕	hàipà	to be afraid
還是	háishì	still is
害羞	hàixiū	shy
好	hǎo	good
河	hé	river
和	hé	with
黑色	hēi (sè)	black
很	hěn	very
後	hòu	rear
花	Huá	Hua (a family name)
換	huàn	to change
皇帝	huángdì	emperor

會	huì	able to		了	le	(indicates completion)
幾	jǐ	a few		累	lèi	tired
劍	jiàn	sword		裡	lǐ	inside
見	jiàn	to see		兩	liǎng	two
剪	jiǎn	to cut		離開	líkāi	go away
將軍	jiāngjūn	General		禮物	lǐwù	gift
叫	jiào	to call, to yell		旅	lǚ	brigade
教	jiào	to teach		馬	mǎ	horse
結束	jiéshù	to finish		媽媽	māmā	mother
進	jìn	to enter		每	měi	each
今天	jīn tian	today		妹妹	mèimei	younger sister
就	jiù	just		沒有	méiyǒu	don't have
家(人)	jjā(rén)	family		們	men	(indicates plural)
軍隊	jūnduì	army		明白	míngbái	to understand
開始	kāishǐ	to start		明天	míngtiān	tomorrow
看	kàn	to look		木蘭	Mùlán	Mulan (a name)
可以	kěyǐ	can		拿	ná	to take
哭	kū	to cry		男孩	nánhái	boy
快	kuài	fast		男人	nánrén	man
來	lái	to come		能	néng	can, able to
老	lǎo	old		年	nián	year

Chinese	Pinyin	English
年輕	niánqīng	young
您	nín	you (respectful)
女	nǚ	female
女孩	nǚhái	girl
怕	pà	afraid
朋友	péngyǒu	friend
漂亮	piàoliang	beautiful
平	Píng	Ping (a name)
Chinese	Pinyin	English
騎	qí	to ride
七	qī	seven
千	qiān	thousand
其他	qítā	other
去	qù	to go with
讓	ràng	to let, to cause
然後	ránhòu	then
人	rén	person, people
山	shān	mountain
上	shàng	on, up
誰	shéi	who
什麼	shénme	what

Chinese	Pinyin	English
身體	shēntǐ	body
十	shí	ten
事	shì	thing, matter
試	shì	to taste, to try
是	shì	yes, is
時(間)	shí(jiān)	time, period
士兵	shìbīng	soldier
手	shǒu	hand
睡	shuì	sleep
說	shuō	to say
說話	shuōhuà	to speak
四	sì	four
死	sǐ	dead, to die
歲	suì	years of age
雖然	suīrán	although
所以	suǒyǐ	and so
他	tā	he, him
它	tā	it
她	tā	she, her
太	tài	too much
逃	táo	to escape

天	tiān	day
條	tiáo	(measure word for narrow, flexible things)
聽	tīng	to listen
頭	tóu	head
頭髮	tóufǎ	hair (on head)
土地	tǔdì	land
晚飯	wǎnfàn	dinner
晚上	wǎnshàng	at night
為	wèi	for
危險	wéixiǎn	danger
問	wèn	to ask
問題	wèntí	problem, question
我	wǒ	I, me
下面	xiàmiàn	below
像	xiàng	to resemble
向	xiàng	towards
想要	xiǎng yào	to want
現在	xiànzài	right now
笑	xiào	to smile
小	xiǎo	small
小隊	xiǎoduì	squad

小心	xiǎoxīn	to be careful
夏天	xiàtiān	summer
鞋	xié	shoes
謝謝	xièxiè	thank you
喜歡	xǐhuān	to like
姓	xìng	surname
星期	xīngqí	week
匈奴	Xiōngnú	Hun people
洗澡	xǐzǎo	to wash
學習	xuéxí	to learn
需要	xūyào	to need
要	yào	to want
要求	yāoqiú	to request
也	yě	also
一	yī	one
一個人	yī gè rén	alone, one person
衣服	yīfú	clothes
以後	yǐhòu	after
已經	yǐjīng	already
營	yíng	camp
贏	yíng	to win

應該	yīnggāi	should
因為	yīnwèi	because
一起	yìqǐ	together
一樣	yíyàng	same
一直	yīzhí	always
用	yòng	to use
右	yòu	right
有	yǒu	to have
有一天	yǒu yītiān	one day
在	zài	in, at
再見	zàijiàn	goodbye
早上	zǎoshang	morning
怎麼	zěnme	how?
站	zhàn	to stand
戰鬥	zhàndòu	fighting
長	zhǎng	leader

帳篷	zhàngpéng	tent
戰士	zhànshì	warrior
著	zhe	with
這	zhè	this
正在	zhèngzài	(-ing)
這些	zhèxiē	these ones
只	zhǐ	only
知道	zhīdào	to know
中	zhōng	in
中國	zhōngguó	China
住在	zhù zài	to live in
準備	zhǔnbèi	ready
總是	zǒng shì	always
走	zǒu	to go
做	zuò	to do
左	zuǒ	left

About the Author

Jeff Pepper (author) is President and CEO of Imagin8 Press, and has written dozens of books about Chinese language and culture. Over his thirty-five year career he has founded and led several successful computer software firms, including one that became a publicly traded company. He's authored two software related books and was awarded three U.S. software patents.

Made in the USA
Las Vegas, NV
20 March 2024